THE BOOK OF HUGS

Illustrations by Kate Cooper

summersdale

THE BOOK OF HUGS

An Hachette UK Company
www.hachette.co.uk

Summersdale Publishers Ltd
Part of Octopus Publishing Group Limited
Carmelite House
50 Victoria Embankment
LONDON
EC4Y 0DZ
UK

www.summersdale.com

Printed and bound in China

ISBN: 978-1-78783-579-5

Substantial discounts on bulk quantities of Summersdale books are available to corporations, professional associations and other organizations. For details contact general enquiries: telephone: +44 (0) 1243 771107 or email: enquiries@summersdale.com.

TO..

FROM............................

A HUG IS WARM

A HUG IS ONE-SIZE-FITS-ALL

A HUG IS
THE BEST CURE

A HUG IS WORTH A THOUSAND WORDS

A HUG IS ENOUGH

A HUG IS FROM THE HEART

A HUG IS
HAPPINESS

A HUG IS
THE ULTIMATE
PASTIME

A HUG IS
MY FAVOURITE
THING

A HUG IS BETTER WHEN SHARED

A HUG IS
ALL YOU NEED
TO FEEL AT EASE

A HUG IS
EFFORTLESS

A HUG IS THE
SAME COME
SUN OR RAIN

A HUG IS ALWAYS THE ANSWER

A HUG IS
LIKE TOUCHING
THE STARS

A HUG IS
BETTER WHEN
YOU SQUEEZE
EXTRA TIGHT!

A HUG IS
AS COSY AS
A HOT DRINK

A HUG IS
A LITTLE PIECE
OF HEAVEN

A HUG IS
LIKE COMING
HOME

A HUG IS PURE JOY

A HUG IS
A SILENT WAY
OF SAYING
"I LOVE YOU"

A HUG IS
THE BEST WAY
TO COMMUNICATE

A HUG IS
A GIFT

A HUG IS LIKE SUNSHINE

A HUG IS NEVER LONG ENOUGH

A HUG IS POWERFUL

A HUG IS FREE!

A HUG IS
THE BEST
INVENTION

A HUG IS IMPOSSIBLE TO GET WRONG

A HUG IS
ALL YOU NEED
TO FEEL ON TOP
OF THE WORLD

IF YOU'RE INTERESTED IN FINDING OUT MORE ABOUT OUR BOOKS, FIND US ON FACEBOOK AT SUMMERSDALE PUBLISHERS AND FOLLOW US ON TWITTER AT @SUMMERSDALE.

WWW.SUMMERSDALE.COM